I-SPY

HORSES AND PONIES

This book belongs to:

Kate Wilkinson

Arab
The Arab is the oldest and purest breed. It is a beautiful, distinctive, and easily recognized horse. It has influenced the development of many of the world's breeds.
I-Spy for **10**

✓

Thoroughbred
The Thoroughbred is renowned in many countries and is a superb racehorse. It has a free action and is brave and tireless. With its good conformation, it plays an important role in producing many of the world's best saddle horses.
I-Spy for **10**

✓

Hanoverian

This horse comes originally from the area around Hanover in Germany. It is intelligent, bold, and active. It shows its ability and athletic qualities when it takes part in showjumping or dressage competitions.
I-Spy for 25

Morgan

The Morgan is a powerful horse which stands between 14.2 and 15.2 hands [a 'hand' is 4 inches (10 cm)]. The breed was established in the United States in the eighteenth century. It makes an attractive and active saddle horse.
I-Spy for 50

Lipizzaner

This breed is used mainly by the Spanish Riding School in Vienna although Lipizzaners can be seen in most European countries. It is a grey with a strong back and quarters, ideally suited to *haute école* (high school), a stylized form of classical riding.
I-Spy for 20

Appaloosa

This is a spotted breed from the United States. The coat may come in different patterns. Not all spotted horses are true Appaloosas.
I-Spy 10 for any spotted horse. Double for an Appaloosa.

Falabella

The smallest horse in the world, the Falabella originated in the Argentine. It must not be more than 30 inches (76.2 cm) at the withers. The Falabella is found in all colours.
I-Spy for **50**

Hackney

The action of the Hackney is its most obvious and attractive characteristic. It is a most spectacular horse and can be seen at shows where carriage driving competitions feature.
I-Spy for **15**

Hunter

A 'type' rather than a breed, a Hunter has good conformation and action as well as jumping ability. In the show ring, classes in several different categories are staged for Hunters.
I-Spy for **15**

Hack

The Hack is a 'type'. A Hack makes an excellent show horse but it requires skilful training and handling to bring out the best of its fine presence, elegance, and free action.
I-Spy for **15**

Cob

Strong and compact, the Cob is a stocky 'type' with powerful legs. It gives a comfortable, if unspectacular, ride as you will see if you watch Cobs being judged in competition.

I-Spy for 15

Shetland

The Shetland is a British native pony breed. It is the smallest of the nine breeds and is perhaps the best known. Shetland ponies are not measured in 'hands', and they stand up to 42 inches (106.7 cm).

I-Spy for 10

7

Highland
A British native pony, the strong-looking Highland is intelligent, sure-footed, and large, usually standing up to 14.2 hands. As its name suggests, it originates from Scotland.
I-Spy for **10** ✓

Welsh Pony
There are four sections of Welsh Pony, the largest being the Welsh Cob. The pony in the picture is a Section B which stands at 13.2 hands. It is very popular as a child's first riding pony.
I-Spy for **10** ✓

Fell

Originating from the northern Pennines and Lake District, Fells were widely used as pack animals to carry heavy loads over the rugged country of northern England.

I-Spy for 20

Dales

The British native Dales Pony is one of the most hardy breeds. It is a strong, sure-footed animal able to carry heavy loads. Today, the breed is used for farm work and for pony trekking.

I-Spy for 15

Exmoor
This is the oldest of the British native ponies and comes from the moorland in south-western England from which it takes its name. Although it is small, the Exmoor is tough and hardy and has great stamina.
I-Spy for 15

Dartmoor
The Dartmoor, a British native, is a useful and adaptable riding pony. It is sure-footed and has a kind, gentle temperament so that it is an excellent child's first pony. Dartmoors are also crossed to produce larger riding ponies.
I-Spy for 10

Connemara

This pony comes from western Ireland but it is classed as a British native breed. The Connemara is versatile and hardy with a natural ability to jump so that it is a popular riding pony.

I-Spy for 10

New Forest

There have been ponies in the New Forest of southern England for more than 1000 years. These ponies are often seen grazing by the roads which cross the forest. They make excellent all-round riding ponies.

I-Spy for 10

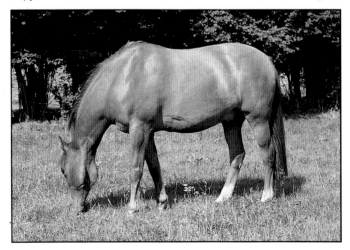

Shire

In recent years, interest in all breeds of heavy horses has been revived greatly. The Shire, one of the strongest yet most gentle of breeds, is especially popular.

I-Spy for 15

Suffolk Punch

Traditionally, this breed is used on farms and as a draught horse. The Suffolk Punch is patient and strong so that it can pull heavy loads. Its origins can be traced back to the early sixteenth century.

I-Spy for 15

Clydesdale

The Clydesdale comes originally from Scotland. It is a very powerful, active breed of heavy horse and has an attractive head. Its main colours are bay, brown, and black with white on the face and limbs.

I-Spy for 15

Cleveland Bay

This breed has been known in the north-eastern district of Yorkshire for more than 200 years. By 1960, few Cleveland Bays were to be seen. Fortunately, their numbers are now increasing.

I-Spy for 20

Percheron

One of the biggest of the French breeds, the Percheron stands up to 17 hands. Mostly grey or black, the breed is widely used as a draught horse.

I-Spy for 25

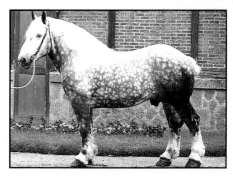

Ardennais

This is a short, stocky, strong draught horse which comes from Ardennes, the region lying on the borders of France and Belgium. Mostly roan, bay, or chestnut, the Ardennais is a willing and hard worker.

I-Spy for 50

Blaze
A Blaze is a distinctive broad white mark which runs down the face from the forehead and between the eyes to the muzzle. A Blaze is more pronounced than the 'stripe', 'snip', or 'white muzzle'.
I-Spy for 10

Snip
A Snip is a narrow white line or mark which runs down the face. It is found on horses and on ponies but must not be confused with other face markings.
I-Spy for 10.
I-Spy 5 extra points for a star, stripe, or white face.

White Stockings
This is the name given to white leg markings which extend as far as the knee or hock. Do not confuse White Stockings with White Socks. The picture shows four Stockings although this marking can be seen on one or two legs.
I-Spy for 10

15

Bay

A Bay horse or pony has a brown body with black mane and tail. It always has black markings on its limbs. The colour Bay is found in most breeds.
I-Spy for 5

Grey

People who are knowledgeable about horses never refer to a 'white' horse. All horses which look white are called Light Grey. As the horse ages, a Grey coat becomes lighter and lighter until it looks almost white.
I-Spy for 10

Palomino

This colour type is applied to horses and ponies which have a cream or golden coat, and a full-flowing mane and tail. The word comes from a breed in the United States. Not all cream horses are true Palominos.
I-Spy for 15

Dappled Grey

Dappled horses and ponies are not very common although many people think of this as the most 'natural' colour. Traditionally, for example, rocking horses are often painted with a Dappled effect.
I-Spy for 20

Skewbald

This name is given to animals in which the body colour has large, irregular patches of white and any colour apart from black.
I-Spy for 10

Piebald

A Piebald horse or pony is one in which the coat is coloured with large, irregular patches of black and white. Do not confuse a Piebald with a Skewbald.
I-Spy for 10

Roan

There are three varieties of the colour Roan: Blue, Strawberry, and Red. The Blue Roan has a black-brown body with some white; the Strawberry Roan has a chestnut body; and the Red Roan a bay-brown colour.
*I-Spy for **10***

Dun

There are two accepted colours: the Yellow Dun and the Blue Dun. A Yellow Dun displays a distinct yellow shade, while the Blue Dun has an amount of black and dark grey to give the 'Blue' effect. Most have stripes on the back.
*I-Spy for **10***

Black

A horse or pony called a 'Black' may have some white on the head and lower limbs but it should always have a black mane and tail. What is the title of a well-known book by Anna Sewell in which the hero is a black horse?

*I-Spy for **10***
Double with answer

Riding Hat

A rider must always wear a properly fitted hard Riding Hat. Since 1990, it has been against the law for anyone under fourteen years old to ride on a public highway without wearing a hard hat. A hard hat should have a chin strap or harness which must be kept fastened.

I-Spy for 5

Post-and-Rail Fencing

This is the best kind of fencing for paddocks and fields where horses and ponies are kept. Hedging or wire are also used around paddocks but these must be checked regularly to make sure that no gaps appear.

I-Spy for 10

Grass-kept
Many horses and ponies can happily be kept out at grass throughout the year if they are given protection in the winter and if they are given food and fresh water daily.
I-Spy for **10** ✓

Water Trough
Clean, fresh water must always be available for a horse or pony. Ideally, a trough filled from a pipe controlled by a ball-cock is the

most efficient. Should water always be available in the stable?

_____

_____

I-Spy for **10**
Double with answer

Headcollar

A Headcollar is made from rope, leather, or nylon, and is used for attaching a lead rope. Ponies which are difficult to catch can graze wearing a Headcollar, but not if the animal is grazing for a long period. Do you know another name for a Headcollar?

I-Spy for **10**
Double with answer ✓

Leading Rein

All young riders, and many beginners, will learn by being led on a Leading Rein. It is fixed to the ring on the side of the Snaffle. Leading Rein classes are held at many shows.

I-Spy for **10** ✓

Bedding
Several different materials are suitable as bedding but the most commonly used is straw. What other materials can be used?

sawdust

I-Spy for 10
Double with answer

Hay
Horses and ponies need a balanced diet, especially during the winter. This can be achieved by feeding Hay for roughage and concentrates or pony cubes for energy.
I-Spy for 5

General-purpose Saddle

Many different types and shapes of saddle are used but the General- or All-purpose Saddle is the most common. It can be used for various equestrian activities. What other saddles can be seen?

dressage

jumping.

Cross country

western

I-Spy for 5
Double with answer

Side Saddle

The Side Saddle is unlike any saddle used when riding astride the horse or pony. It is designed with two pommels, so that the rider can sit with both legs on the near side. This is called riding side-saddle.
I-Spy for 15

Double Bridle
The Double Bridle or Weymouth is one of five groupings of bridle which include the Snaffle, Pelham, Gag, and Bitless. All bridles have a headpiece, throatlash, cheek pieces, browband, and noseband.

I-Spy for 5

Snaffle Bit
The Snaffle is the simplest bit and is made from metal, rubber, or vulcanite, with a straight or jointed mouthpiece. Single reins are attached to the rings.
I-Spy for 5

Flash Noseband

Where a standing martingale is used, the Flash Noseband is often introduced. This is a normal cavesson with two straps attached to the sides which are crossed and fastened under the bit.

I-Spy for 10

Stirrups

Stirrup Irons, into which the rider places his or her feet, are made from metal and hang from Stirrup Leathers which are attached to the saddle, under the flap.

I-Spy for 5

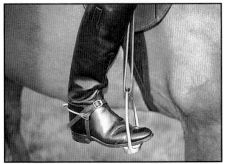

Run-up Stirrups

Stirrups are Run-up to prevent them from flapping and possibly causing injury. Immediately on dismounting, both irons should be left as shown in the photograph.

I-Spy for 5

Knee Guard

Sometimes known as Knee Caps, Knee Guards are made from padded felt with leather fastening straps. They are especially valuable when exercising, and essential when travelling.

I-Spy for 10

Brushing Boots and Over-reach Boots

A horse can be injured when jumping if a hind shoe catches on or above the heel of the foot in front. Over-reach Boots are fitted to prevent this. Anti-brushing Boots are also used for protection.

Over-reach Boots

Anti-brushing Boots

I-Spy 10 for each

Tail Bandage

A Tail Bandage is fitted to prevent rubbing or injury when the horse is travelling. It is usually made from crêpe or stockinette material and must be removed at the end of the journey.
I-Spy for 10

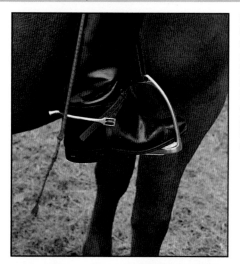

Spurs

Many kinds of Spurs are available. They are used to reinforce the leg 'aid'. The neck of the Spurs must always point downwards, and preferably should be blunt ended.

I-Spy for **10** ✓

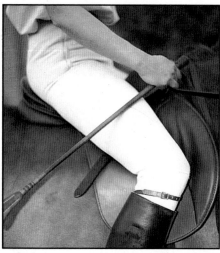

Whip

The Whip or Stick is an artificial aid used to support the rider's leg action. It is carried across the thigh and should point downwards. What is the maximum length of Whip used when showjumping?

_____

_____

I-Spy for **5** ✓
Double with answer

Grooming

The Body Brush and Curry Comb are shown in the photograph. The Comb is used to clean the dust from the Brush. The other equipment used for grooming include: Hoof Pick, Dandy Brush, Water Brush, Wisp, Rubber.

I-Spy 5 for each one you see.

✓ ✓ ✓ ✓ ✓

Hunter Clip

Depending on the amount of work its gets during the winter, a horse or pony will usually need Clipping. If this is not done, the animal will sweat-up and lose condition. Name one other type of Clip.

<u>trace clip.</u>

I-Spy for 10 – double with answer

✓

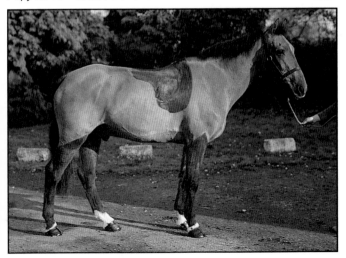

Plaiting

The mane of a horse or pony is Plaited for neatness and to show off the neck and crest. There should be an uneven number of Plaits down the neck, and an extra one at the forelock.

I-Spy for 10

Bran Mash

Bran Mash is one of the best feeds to give after hard work or exercise. It is made by half filling a bucket with bran, adding a pinch of salt, and pouring on boiling water. Stir the Mash into a smooth paste, cover it with sacking, and serve when cool.

I-Spy for 10

New Zealand Rug
This is one of the most commonly used items of protective clothing for horses and ponies. It is made from stout, lined, waterproof material and the animal wears it during the winter. What is the colour of a New Zealand Rug?

green.

I-Spy for 5 ✓
Double with answer

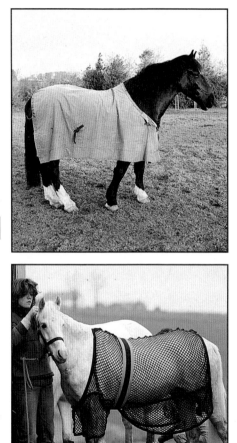

Anti-sweat Sheet
This is one kind of sheet and blanket worn by horses and ponies. An Anti-sweat Sheet is made from cotton mesh and is put on after work or exercise to prevent the horse becoming chilled.
I-Spy for 5 ✓

31

Lungeing

This is the method of giving horses and ponies controlled exercise without them being ridden. The Lunge Rein is attached to a specially designed cavesson.
I-Spy for 15

✓

Rosettes

The number of Rosettes awarded in competition will depend upon the number of competitors taking part. In showing classes, more than one Rosette can be won. What is the usual colour of a First Place Rosette?

Red

I-Spy for 10
Double with answer

✓

Farrier

A Farrier, or Blacksmith, is the highly skilled person who makes and fits shoes, and who is able to give advice on the condition of horses' feet. Which tool is used when removing a shoe?

I-Spy for 25
Double with answer ✓

Trailers

Trailers are built to carry one or two horses or ponies. To ease loading and unloading, they are sometimes designed with a rear and side opening and ramp.
I-Spy for 15 ✓

Horse Box

There is a wide variety of Horse Boxes available, from those which carry one or two horses to the bigger Boxes which can carry eight or more.
I-Spy for 15 ✓

Four-in-Hand
The front two horses of a Four-in-Hand are known as the 'leaders', and the two nearer the coach the 'wheelers'. The four horses are controlled by the 'whip', the name given to the person driving.
I-Spy for 30

Ploughing
Horses are still used in many parts of the country for Ploughing. In fact, many farmers believe they are far more efficient than the modern tractor.
I-Spy for 30

Police
Throughout the world, Police Forces have mounted sections. Their duties include crowd control, traffic control, and general police work.
I-Spy for 15

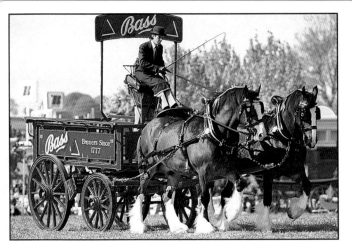

Brewer's Dray

Teams of heavy horses are still used in some parts of Britain to transport goods. In many cities, the Brewer's Dray can be seen delivering beer.

I-Spy for 30

Trade Turnout

A popular display is that staged for a Coster Turnout, sometimes called the Trade Classes. Single horses and pairs can be seen pulling traditional vehicles, many of which are in daily use.

I-Spy for 25

Household Cavalry

The drum horse here is leading a display of the Household Cavalry. Traditionally, the Household Cavalry escorts the sovereign on state and ceremonial occasions.

I-Spy for 20

Pony Club

The Pony Club, part of the British Horse Society, was founded in 1929. It has some 367 branches in Britain, and 1750 branches in other countries. Membership is open to boys and girls up to twenty-one years old.

I-Spy for 10

Spider Phaeton

The Spider Phaeton is one of the most elegant of the many types of vehicles which are used in carriage driving competitions today. It was first introduced more than 100 years ago.

I-Spy for 25

Mail Coach

During the nineteenth century, the only way in which mail could be carried from one city to another was by Mail Coach. Today, there are several which can still be seen on the roads as they travel to shows and displays.

I-Spy for 50

Some plants, shrubs, and the fruits of certain trees are dangerous to horses if the animals eat too much of them. Others may be hazardous or even fatal even in only small amounts.

Ragwort

The clusters of bright-yellow flowers may be seen along roadsides, in badly tended pastures, or in all kinds of waste places from June to November. Ragwort, which can kill horses or other stock, is especially dangerous when the top of the plant is broken off and left to die.
I-Spy for 5
Treble if you dig it up and destroy it.

Hemlock

Hemlock is similar in appearance to the well-known Cow Parsley. It is usually found in damp meadows or open woodland near ponds or streams. It flowers between May and June but it is not very common. In small quantities, a drink made from Hemlock is a powerful sleeping draught but in larger amounts, it can kill people as well as animals.
I-Spy for 20

Oak

Almost everyone can recognize an Oak tree and its fruit the acorn. Traditionally, pigs were turned out into woods to forage for the nuts of trees like the Oak or Beech but if horses eat too many acorns, this can be dangerous to them.
I-Spy for 10 ✓

Laurel

In this case, it is the Cherry Laurel, and not the Sweet Bay Laurel, which need concern us. The spear-shaped, leathery, shiny green leaves and the seeds smell of bitter almonds and contain a poison which is similar to hydrogen cyanide or prussic acid.
I-Spy for 10

Showjumping

There are Showjumping competitions for riders of all ages and abilities. The courses are designed and built for indoor or outdoor arenas. What are the penalties for (a) a knock-down? (b) a refusal?

(a) _____

_____

(b) _____

_____

*I-Spy for **10***
Double with answers

Dressage

Dressage is the art of training horses in obedience, deportment, and responses. There are competitions specially devised and held for Dressage enthusiasts from novice levels to the most advanced, but Dressage is also one of the three disciplines of horse and driving trials.
*I-Spy for **15***

Cross-country
As with Dressage, Cross-country is one of the three disciplines, or phases, included at horse trials. All obstacles are fixed and are not built to be knocked down, unlike those used for Showjumping.
I-Spy for **10** ✓

Side-saddle
For many hundreds of years, ladies have ridden side-saddle, although the saddle we see today did not appear until the early part of the nineteenth century.
I-Spy for **20** ✓

41

John Whitaker

Many remember John as the partner of the great Ryan's Son, one of the most successful combinations ever. In recent times, he has achieved considerable success on the popular Henderson Milton.
*I-Spy for **15***

↓ Michael Whitaker

Younger brother of John, Michael has been a member of the British team for several years. Among his many achievements was his membership of the winning Nations' Cup teams in 1990.
*I-Spy for **15***

← Marie Edgar

Daughter of Ted and Liz Edgar, Marie was born in 1970. For one so young, she has enjoyed outstanding success as a Showjumper, and has represented her country many times. What is the relationship between Liz Edgar and David Broome?

*I-Spy for **15** – double with answer*

Pierre Durand
One of the top Showjumpers from France, Pierre is often seen at the major shows in Britain and elsewhere. He is seen here with his great horse, Jappaloupe.

I-Spy for **25**

Mark Todd
This popular, top-class horse-man was born in New Zealand. He has competed in many countries throughout the world. He is acknowledged to be among the best Event riders and has won two Olympic Gold Medals at Horse Trials.

I-Spy for **15**

Anni MacDonald-Hall

A comparative newcomer to equestrian sport, Anni has had an outstanding success in the demanding world of Dressage. She was a member of the British team at Stockholm and won the title of National Champion in 1990.

I-Spy for 20

Milton

This most successful jumper of recent times is owned by Mr and Mrs J T Bradley. He has appeared in many countries and is loved by the crowds who flock to see him.

I-Spy for 15

Polo

Polo is a ball game for two teams of four mounted players. The game consists of five or six periods, or chukkas, each of which lasts for 7¹/₂ minutes. Polo may be the world's oldest recorded game, and was first played in England in 1869.

I-Spy for 30

Carriage Driving

Bringing back the horse-drawn carriage has added an attractive feature to the equestrian scene. Three-day trials are similar in their arrangement to eventing: Dressage, marathon, and a speed competition over a twisting course of cones.

I-Spy for 25

Horseracing — Flat

Horses raced over a track with no jumps cover distances of between 5 and 11 furlongs (a furlong is 220 yards or just over 200 metres). The best-known British flat race is the Derby, held in June. What is the name of the fillies' race also held at Epsom?

*I-Spy for **10** – double with answer*

Steeplechasing

For many people, this is the most exciting type of racing, made world famous by the Grand National. It requires great ability and courage from horse and rider alike to tackle the formidable-looking obstacles and water jump.
*I-Spy for **10***

Hurdle Racing

Racing over hurdles began early in the nineteenth century. The distance raced can be up to 3 miles (about 4.8 km). There are not more than four hurdles in each mile, and each hurdle is 3 feet 6 inches (just over 1 m) high.
I-Spy for 10

Point-to-Point

It is thought that early Point-to-Point races took place over a course measured between the point of one church steeple and another. Today, meetings are organized by Hunts and the season is from February to May.
I-Spy for 25

Trotting

Trotting, or Harness Racing, is a form of Driving in which the horse pulls a sulky, a two-wheeled vehicle, in which the driver (not a jockey) sits.
I-Spy for 25

INDEX

Appaloosa 4
Arab 2
Ardennais 14

Bay 16
Bedding 22
Bit, Snaffle 24
Black 18
Blaze 15
Boots, Brushing 27
Boots, Over-reach 27
Bran Mash 30
Bridle, Double 24

Carriage Driving 45
Cavalry, Household 36
Cleveland Bay 13
Clip, Hunter 29
Clydesdale 13
Coach, Mail 37
Cob 7
Connemara 11
Cross-country 41

Dales 9
Dappled Grey 17
Dartmoor 10
Dray, Brewer's 35
Dressage 40
Dun 18
Durand, Pierre 43

Edgar, Marie 42
Exmoor 10

Falabella 5
Farrier 33
Fell 9
Fencing, Post-and-Rail 19
Four-in-Hand 34

Grass-kept 20
Grey 16
Grooming 29

Hack 6
Hackney 5
Hanoverian 3

Hay 22
Headcollar 21
Hemlock 38
Highland 8
Horse Box 33
Horseracing — Flat 46
Hunter 6
Hurdle Racing 47

Knee Guard 26

Laurel 39
Lipizanner 4
Lungeing 32

MacDonald-Hall, Anni 44
Milton 44
Morgan 3

New Forest 11
Noseband, Flash 25

Oak 39

Palomino 16
Percheron 14
Piebald 17
Plaiting 30
Ploughing 34
Point-to-Point 47
Poisonous Plants 38-9
Police 34
Polo 45
Pony Club 36

Ragwort 38
Rein, Leading 21
Riding Hat 19
Roan 18
Rosette 32
Rug, New Zealand 31

Saddle, General-purpose 23
Saddle, Side 23
Sheet, Anti-sweat 31
Shetland 7
Shire 12
Showjumping 40

Side-saddle 41
Skewbald 17
Snip 15
Spider Phaeton 37
Spurs 28
Steeplechasing 46
Stirrups 25
Stirrups, Run-up 26
Suffolk Punch 12

Tail Bandage 27
Thoroughbred 2
Todd, Mark 43
Trade Turnout 35
Trailer 33
Trotting 47

Water Trough 20
Welsh Pony 8
Whip 28
Whitaker, John 42
Whitaker, Michael 42
White Stockings 15

Answers

Black: *Black Beauty*.
Water Trough: Yes.
Headcollar: Halter.
Bedding: Wood Chippings,
Shredded Paper, Sawdust.
General-purpose Saddle:
Dressage, Show, Side
Saddle, Racing Saddle.
Whip: 30 inches (75 cm).
Rosette: Red.
New Zealand Rug: Green.
Farrier: Pincers.
Showjumping: (a) 4 faults; (b)
3 for the first, 6 for the
second, at the third
elimination.
Marie Edgar: Brother and
Sister.
Horseracing — Flat: the Oaks.

© I-Spy Limited 1991

ISBN (paperback) 1 85671 049 1
ISBN (hard cover) 1 85671 050 5

Michelin Tyre Public Limited Company
Davy House, Lyon Road, Harrow, Middlesex HA1 2DQ

MICHELIN and the Michelin Man are Registered Trademarks of Michelin Tyre plc

A CIP record for this title is available from the British Library.

Edited and designed by Curtis Garratt Limited, The Old Vicarage, Horton cum Studley, Oxford OX9 1BT

The Publisher gratefully acknowledges the contribution of Kit Houghton who provided the majority of the photographs in this I-Spy book. Additional photographs by Robert Owen who also wrote the text.

Colour reproduction by Norwich Litho Services Limited.

Printed in Spain.